THE BEGINNING

Dear Reader,
I'm writing this verse just for you,
Please colour the pictures,
And read it right through.

If, by chance,
You began at the end,
This book, Dear Reader,
Still makes you my friend.

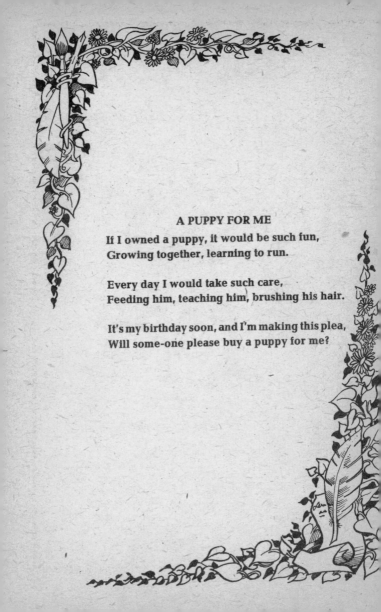

A PUPPY FOR ME

If I owned a puppy, it would be such fun,
Growing together, learning to run.

Every day I would take such care,
Feeding him, teaching him, brushing his hair.

It's my birthday soon, and I'm making this plea,
Will some-one please buy a puppy for me?

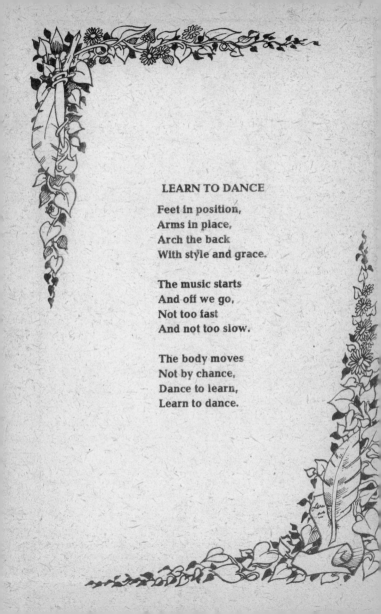

LEARN TO DANCE

Feet in position,
Arms in place,
Arch the back
With style and grace.

The music starts
And off we go,
Not too fast
And not too slow.

The body moves
Not by chance,
Dance to learn,
Learn to dance.

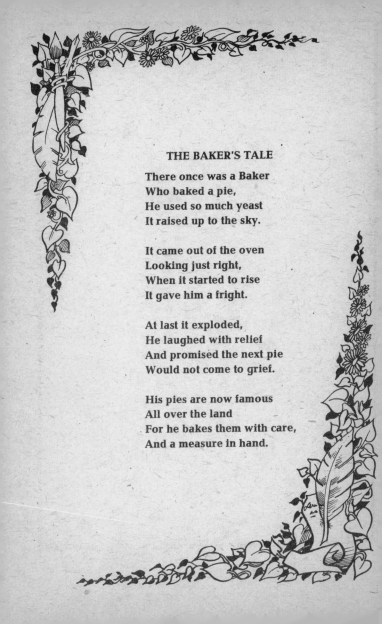

THE BAKER'S TALE

There once was a Baker
Who baked a pie,
He used so much yeast
It raised up to the sky.

It came out of the oven
Looking just right,
When it started to rise
It gave him a fright.

At last it exploded,
He laughed with relief
And promised the next pie
Would not come to grief.

His pies are now famous
All over the land
For he bakes them with care,
And a measure in hand.

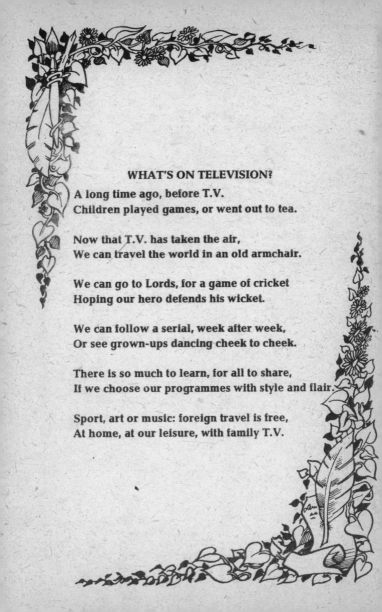

WHAT'S ON TELEVISION?

A long time ago, before T.V.
Children played games, or went out to tea.

Now that T.V. has taken the air,
We can travel the world in an old armchair.

We can go to Lords, for a game of cricket
Hoping our hero defends his wicket.

We can follow a serial, week after week,
Or see grown-ups dancing cheek to cheek.

There is so much to learn, for all to share,
If we choose our programmes with style and flair.

Sport, art or music: foreign travel is free,
At home, at our leisure, with family T.V.

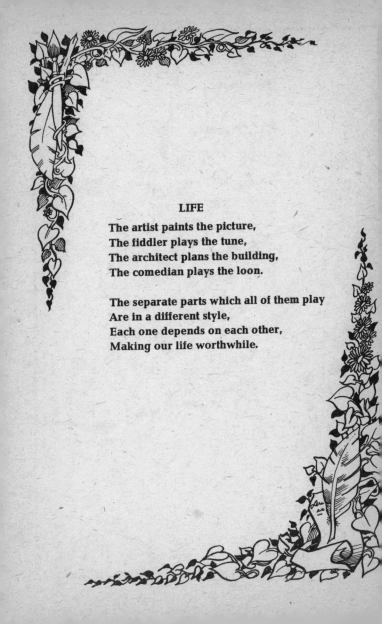

LIFE

The artist paints the picture,
The fiddler plays the tune,
The architect plans the building,
The comedian plays the loon.

The separate parts which all of them play
Are in a different style,
Each one depends on each other,
Making our life worthwhile.

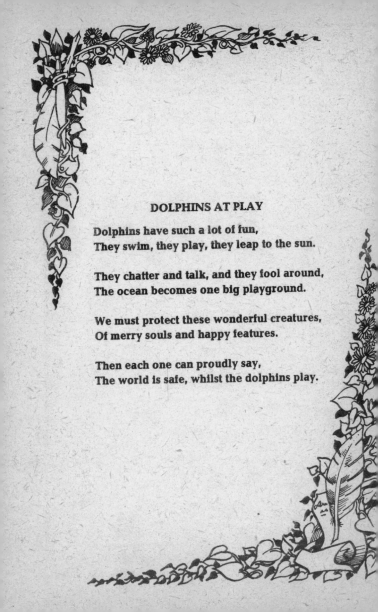

DOLPHINS AT PLAY

Dolphins have such a lot of fun,
They swim, they play, they leap to the sun.

They chatter and talk, and they fool around,
The ocean becomes one big playground.

We must protect these wonderful creatures,
Of merry souls and happy features.

Then each one can proudly say,
The world is safe, whilst the dolphins play.

PENGUIN PARTY

O what a party
That would be,
With all my friends
Surrounding me,
And a penguin
Just to serve the tea,
O what a party
That would be!

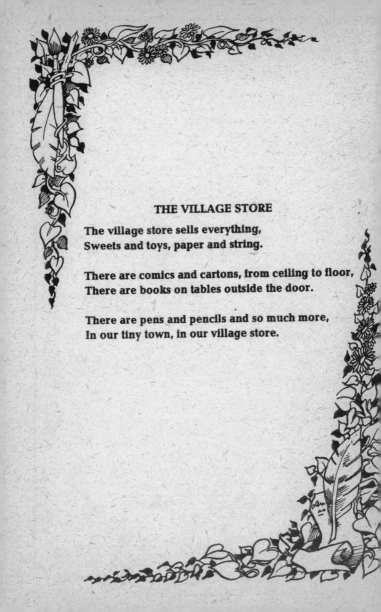

THE VILLAGE STORE

The village store sells everything,
Sweets and toys, paper and string.

There are comics and cartons, from ceiling to floor,
There are books on tables outside the door.

There are pens and pencils and so much more,
In our tiny town, in our village store.

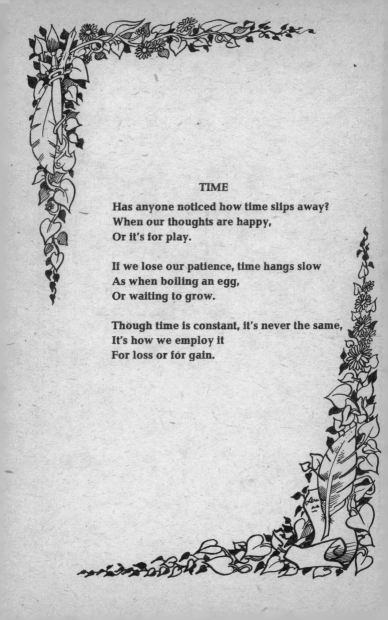

TIME

Has anyone noticed how time slips away?
When our thoughts are happy,
Or it's for play.

If we lose our patience, time hangs slow
As when boiling an egg,
Or waiting to grow.

Though time is constant, it's never the same,
It's how we employ it
For loss or for gain.

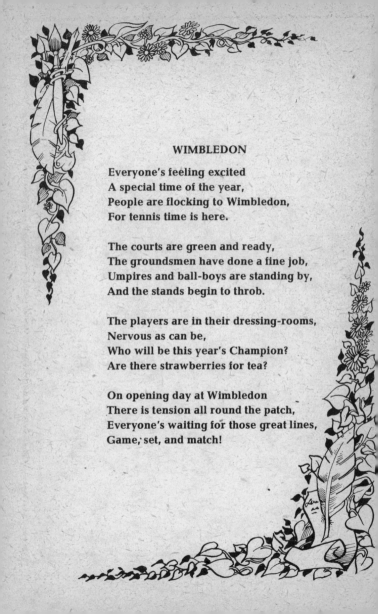

WIMBLEDON

Everyone's feeling excited
A special time of the year,
People are flocking to Wimbledon,
For tennis time is here.

The courts are green and ready,
The groundsmen have done a fine job,
Umpires and ball-boys are standing by,
And the stands begin to throb.

The players are in their dressing-rooms,
Nervous as can be,
Who will be this year's Champion?
Are there strawberries for tea?

On opening day at Wimbledon
There is tension all round the patch,
Everyone's waiting for those great lines,
Game, set, and match!

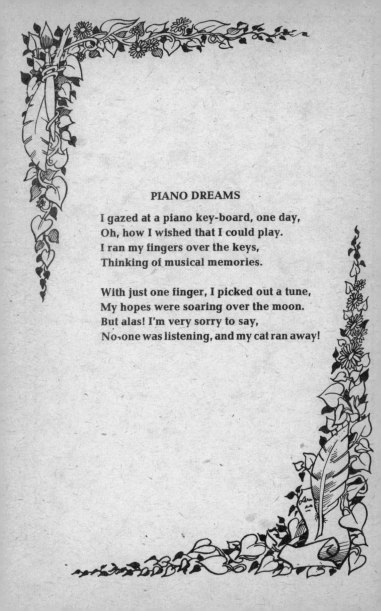

PIANO DREAMS

I gazed at a piano key-board, one day,
Oh, how I wished that I could play.
I ran my fingers over the keys,
Thinking of musical memories.

With just one finger, I picked out a tune,
My hopes were soaring over the moon.
But alas! I'm very sorry to say,
No-one was listening, and my cat ran away!

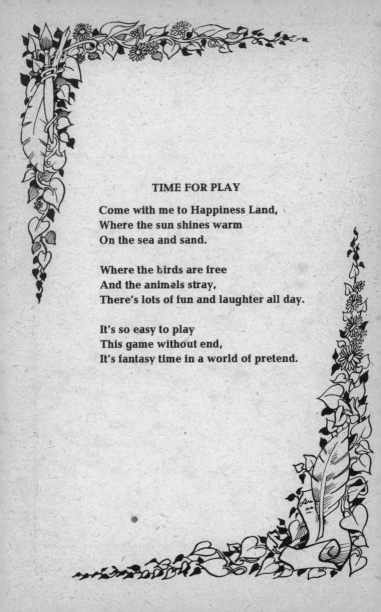

TIME FOR PLAY

Come with me to Happiness Land,
Where the sun shines warm
On the sea and sand.

Where the birds are free
And the animals stray,
There's lots of fun and laughter all day.

It's so easy to play
This game without end,
It's fantasy time in a world of pretend.

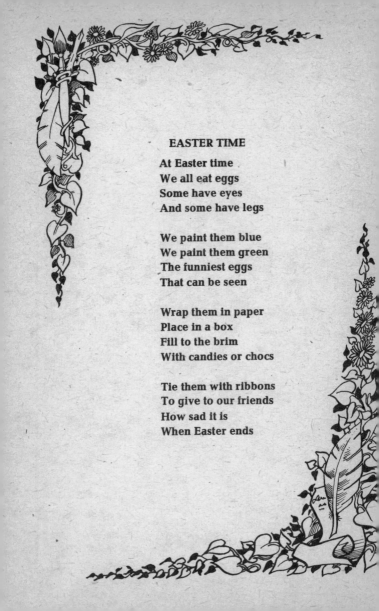

EASTER TIME

At Easter time
We all eat eggs
Some have eyes
And some have legs

We paint them blue
We paint them green
The funniest eggs
That can be seen

Wrap them in paper
Place in a box
Fill to the brim
With candies or chocs

Tie them with ribbons
To give to our friends
How sad it is
When Easter ends

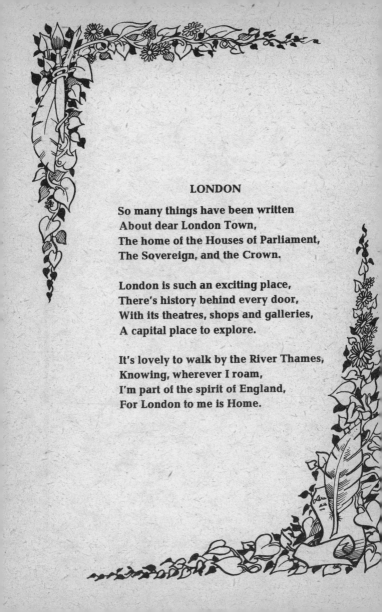

LONDON

So many things have been written
About dear London Town,
The home of the Houses of Parliament,
The Sovereign, and the Crown.

London is such an exciting place,
There's history behind every door,
With its theatres, shops and galleries,
A capital place to explore.

It's lovely to walk by the River Thames,
Knowing, wherever I roam,
I'm part of the spirit of England,
For London to me is Home.

RIDING MY BICYCLE

Riding my bike
Can be such fun,
With the wind in my hair
And my face in the sun.

The wheels go round
And I'm on my way,
My thoughts are light
As the miles slip away.

I take great care
When I'm on the road,
Observing the rules
Of the Highway Code.

When I'm rolling along
My heart is singing,
My bike's my friend
And my bell is ringing.

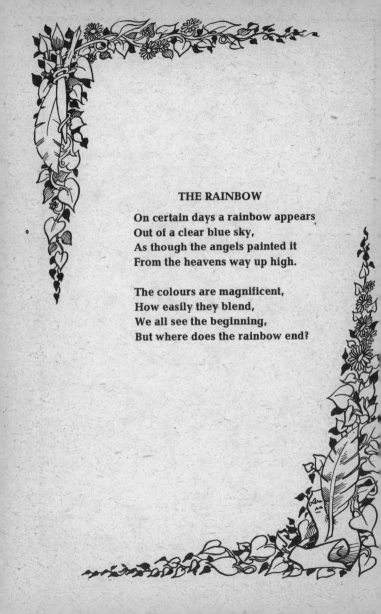

THE RAINBOW

On certain days a rainbow appears
Out of a clear blue sky,
As though the angels painted it
From the heavens way up high.

The colours are magnificent,
How easily they blend,
We all see the beginning,
But where does the rainbow end?

ON THE FARM

Dogs bark,
Cows moo,
The rooster crows
Cock-a-doodle-do!

A tractor roars,
The hens go crazy,
Down on the farm
Is no place for the lazy.

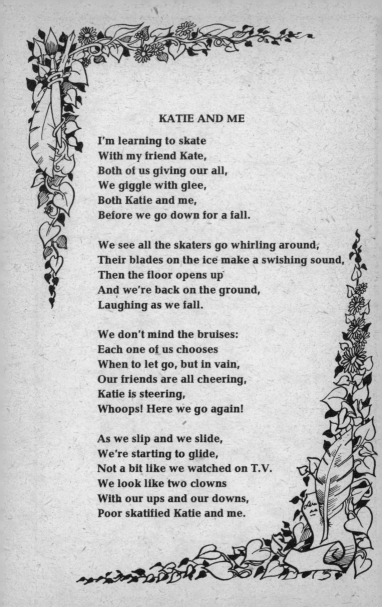

KATIE AND ME

I'm learning to skate
With my friend Kate,
Both of us giving our all,
We giggle with glee,
Both Katie and me,
Before we go down for a fall.

We see all the skaters go whirling around,
Their blades on the ice make a swishing sound,
Then the floor opens up
And we're back on the ground,
Laughing as we fall.

We don't mind the bruises:
Each one of us chooses
When to let go, but in vain,
Our friends are all cheering,
Katie is steering,
Whoops! Here we go again!

As we slip and we slide,
We're starting to glide,
Not a bit like we watched on T.V.
We look like two clowns
With our ups and our downs,
Poor skatified Katie and me.

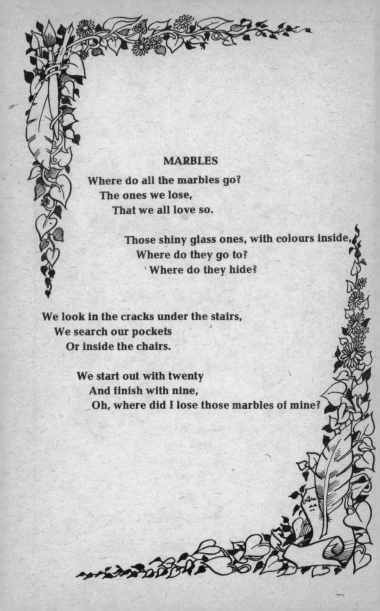

MARBLES

Where do all the marbles go?
The ones we lose,
That we all love so.

Those shiny glass ones, with colours inside,
Where do they go to?
Where do they hide?

We look in the cracks under the stairs,
We search our pockets
Or inside the chairs.

We start out with twenty
And finish with nine,
Oh, where did I lose those marbles of mine?

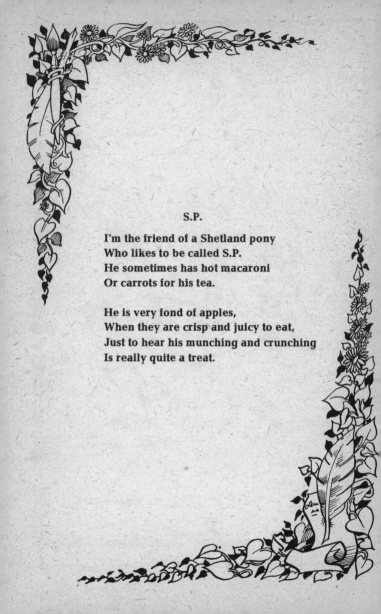

S.P.

I'm the friend of a Shetland pony
Who likes to be called S.P.
He sometimes has hot macaroni
Or carrots for his tea.

He is very fond of apples,
When they are crisp and juicy to eat,
Just to hear his munching and crunching
Is really quite a treat.

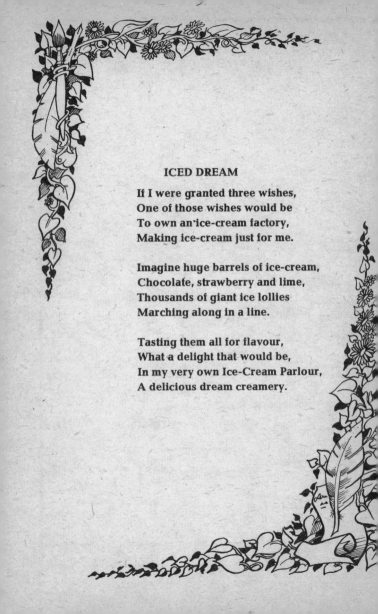

ICED DREAM

If I were granted three wishes,
One of those wishes would be
To own an ice-cream factory,
Making ice-cream just for me.

Imagine huge barrels of ice-cream,
Chocolate, strawberry and lime,
Thousands of giant ice lollies
Marching along in a line.

Tasting them all for flavour,
What a delight that would be,
In my very own Ice-Cream Parlour,
A delicious dream creamery.

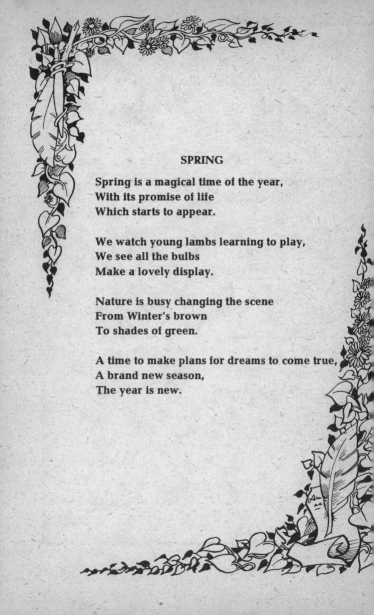

SPRING

Spring is a magical time of the year,
With its promise of life
Which starts to appear.

We watch young lambs learning to play,
We see all the bulbs
Make a lovely display.

Nature is busy changing the scene
From Winter's brown
To shades of green.

A time to make plans for dreams to come true,
A brand new season,
The year is new.

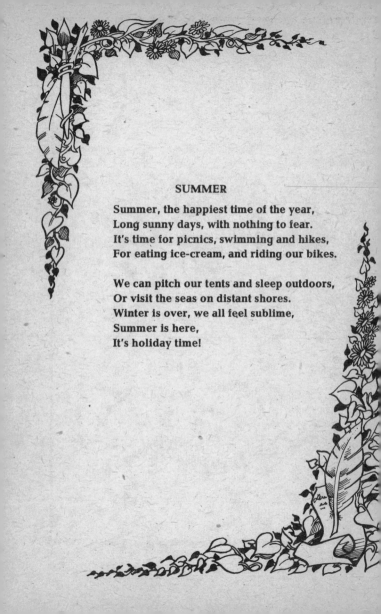

SUMMER

Summer, the happiest time of the year,
Long sunny days, with nothing to fear.
It's time for picnics, swimming and hikes,
For eating ice-cream, and riding our bikes.

We can pitch our tents and sleep outdoors,
Or visit the seas on distant shores.
Winter is over, we all feel sublime,
Summer is here,
It's holiday time!

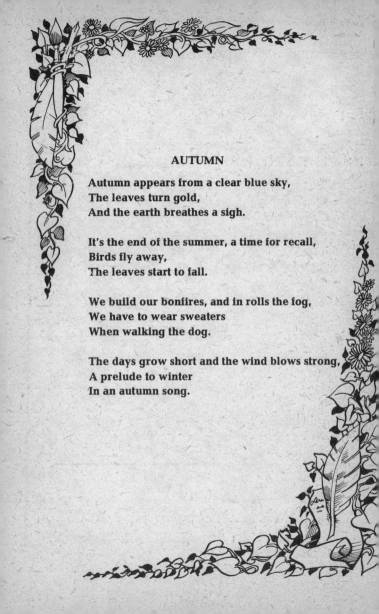

AUTUMN

Autumn appears from a clear blue sky,
The leaves turn gold,
And the earth breathes a sigh.

It's the end of the summer, a time for recall,
Birds fly away,
The leaves start to fall.

We build our bonfires, and in rolls the fog,
We have to wear sweaters
When walking the dog.

The days grow short and the wind blows strong,
A prelude to winter
In an autumn song.

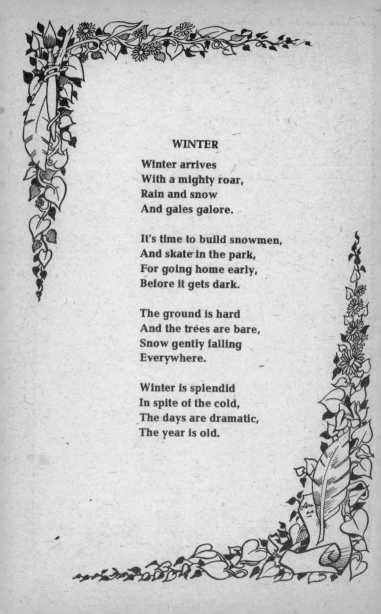

WINTER

Winter arrives
With a mighty roar,
Rain and snow
And gales galore.

It's time to build snowmen,
And skate in the park,
For going home early,
Before it gets dark.

The ground is hard
And the trees are bare,
Snow gently falling
Everywhere.

Winter is splendid
In spite of the cold,
The days are dramatic,
The year is old.

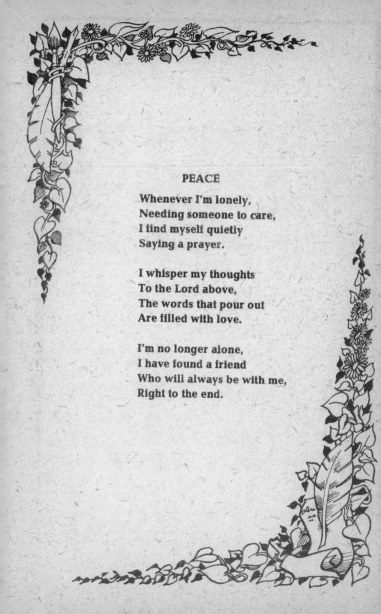

PEACE

Whenever I'm lonely,
Needing someone to care,
I find myself quietly
Saying a prayer.

I whisper my thoughts
To the Lord above,
The words that pour out
Are filled with love.

I'm no longer alone,
I have found a friend
Who will always be with me,
Right to the end.

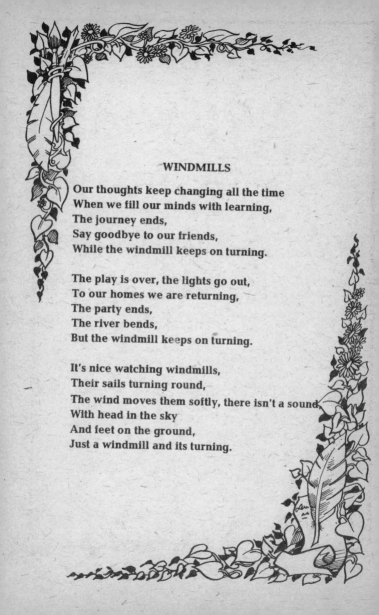

WINDMILLS

Our thoughts keep changing all the time
When we fill our minds with learning,
The journey ends,
Say goodbye to our friends,
While the windmill keeps on turning.

The play is over, the lights go out,
To our homes we are returning,
The party ends,
The river bends,
But the windmill keeps on turning.

It's nice watching windmills,
Their sails turning round,
The wind moves them softly, there isn't a sound,
With head in the sky
And feet on the ground,
Just a windmill and its turning.

A SUNNY DAY

The sea came rolling in,
　　And the sun was in the sky,
　　　Way out on the horizon
　　　　A ship went sailing by.

I tossed a pebble in the water,
　　Without a single care,
　　　There was laughter all around me,
　　　　And happiness to spare.

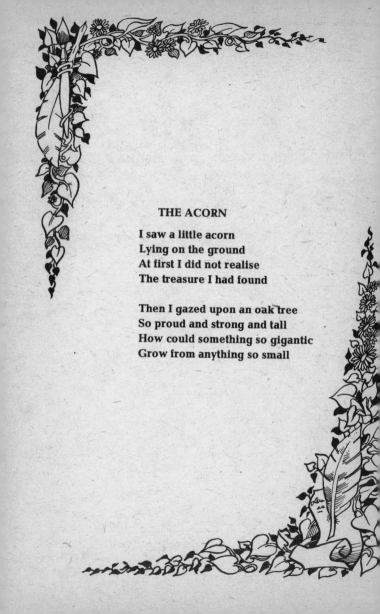

THE ACORN

I saw a little acorn
Lying on the ground
At first I did not realise
The treasure I had found

Then I gazed upon an oak tree
So proud and strong and tall
How could something so gigantic
Grow from anything so small

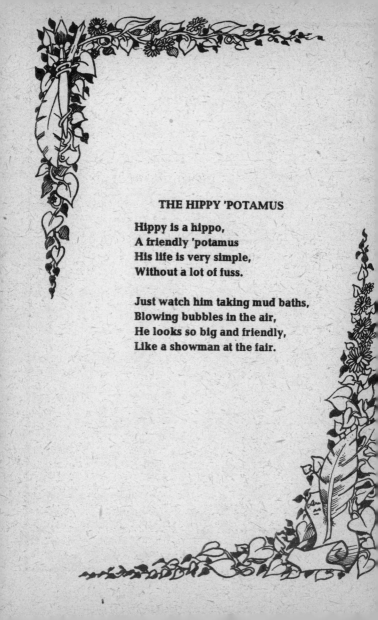

THE HIPPY 'POTAMUS

Hippy is a hippo,
A friendly 'potamus
His life is very simple,
Without a lot of fuss.

Just watch him taking mud baths,
Blowing bubbles in the air,
He looks so big and friendly,
Like a showman at the fair.

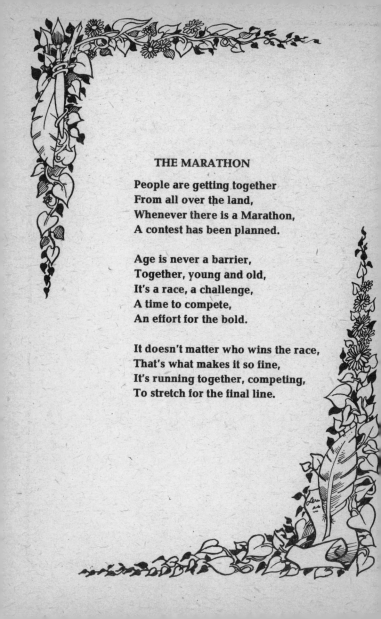

THE MARATHON

People are getting together
From all over the land,
Whenever there is a Marathon,
A contest has been planned.

Age is never a barrier,
Together, young and old,
It's a race, a challenge,
A time to compete,
An effort for the bold.

It doesn't matter who wins the race,
That's what makes it so fine,
It's running together, competing,
To stretch for the final line.

THE END

Elphin Lloyd-Jones drew the pictures,
Barbara provided the rhyme,
The Publisher put it together,
We all hope you've had a good time.

PRINTED IN POLAND
FOR THE PUBLISHERS PETER HADDOCK LTD.
BRIDLINGTON, ENGLAND